ESCAPE

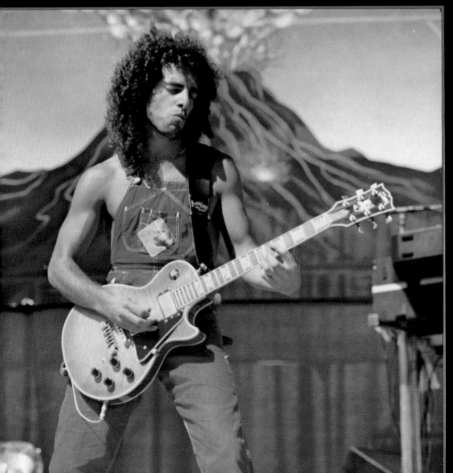

DON'T STOP BELIEVIN'

Moderately

Words and Music by
S. PERRY, N. SCHON and
J. CAIN

1. Just a   small town   girl,__   liv - in' in a
2. Just a   cit - y   boy,__   born and raised in
3. Voice tacet
4. 5. 6. (see additional lyrics)

Don't Stop Believin' - 5 - 1

6

Don't Stop Believin' - 5 - 2

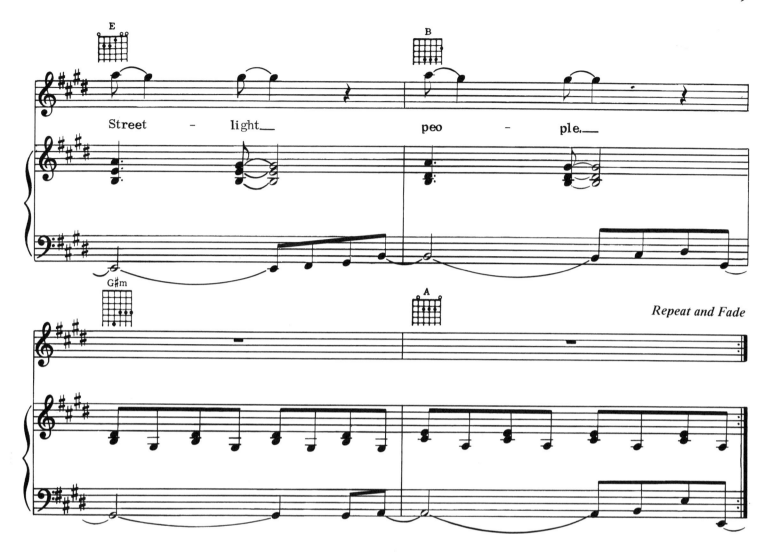

Street - light___ peo - ple.___

Repeat and Fade

Verse 4:
A singer in a smokey room;
The smell of wine and cheap perfume.
For a smile they can share the night;
It goes on and on and on and on.

Verse 5:
Working hard to get my fill;
Everybody wants a thrill.
Payin' anything to roll the dice,
Just one more time.

Verse 6:
Some will win, some will lose,
Some were born to sing the blues.
Oh, the movie never ends,
It goes on and on and on and on.

STONE IN LOVE

Words and Music by
S. PERRY, N. SCHON and
J. CAIN

Stone In Love - 4 - 1

best times ___ most ___ of all. ___

(3rd time guitar solo)
In the heat ___ with a blue jean girl; ___

burn-in' love comes once in a life - time.

She found me sing-ing by the rail - road track; ___

took me home; we danced by the moon - light. Those sum - mer nights

(end solo)

— are call - in'; stone in — love.—

Can't help my- self — I'm fall - in'; stone in — love.—

1. D.C. 2. D.S. 3.

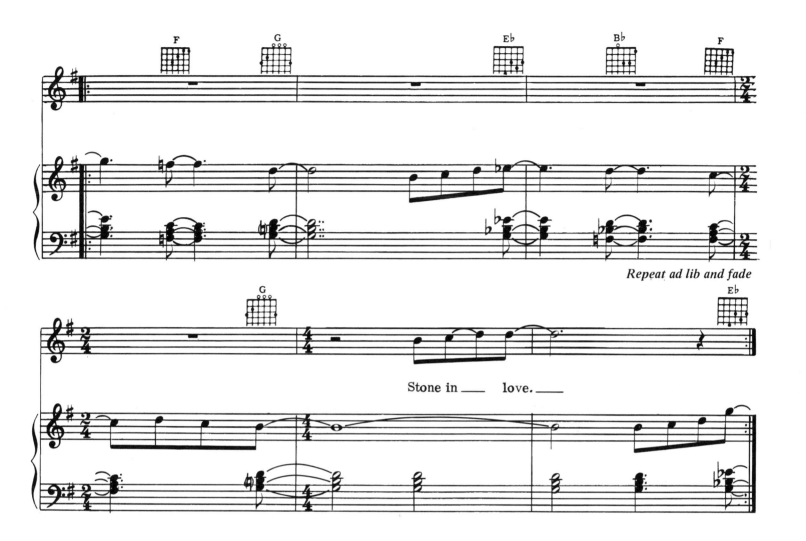

Repeat ad lib and fade

Stone in ___ love. ___

Verse 2:
Old dusty roads led to the river;
Runnin' slow.
She pulled me down, and in clover,
We'd go 'round.
In the heat with a blue jean girl;
Burnin' love comes once in a lifetime.
Oh, the memories never fade away;
Golden girl, I'll keep you forever.

WHO'S CRYING NOW

Words and Music by
S. PERRY and J. CAIN

Moderately

1. It's been a mys-ter-y,_____ and still they
2. Caught on a one-way street,_____ the taste of
3. 4. *(see additional lyrics)*

try to see_____ why some-thing good can hurt_____ so_____ bad._____
bit-ter-sweet;_____ love will sur-vive some-how,_____ some -

Who's Crying Now - 3 - 1

Verse 3:
So many stormy nights,
So many wrongs or rights;
Neither could change their headstrong ways.

Verse 4:
And in a lover's rage,
They tore another page.
The fighting is worth the love they save.

KEEP ON RUNNIN'

Words and Music by
S. PERRY, N. SCHON and
J. CAIN

Bright Rock and Roll

1. Work-in' in the cit - y this town's got no pit - y;
2.3. (see additional lyrics)
4. (instr. solo, ad lib)

boss - man owns a heart of stone.

Keep On Runnin' - 4 - 1

20

Verse 2:
They get me by the hour,
By my blue collar.
You're squeezing me too tight,
It's Friday night;
Let's run tonight
Till the morning light.

Verse 3:
Cruising with my baby,
Think we just might, maybe
Find some back seat rhythm and blues.
Radio; down we go, down we go.

STILL THEY RIDE

Words and Music by
S. PERRY, N. SCHON and
J. CAIN

Still They Ride - 2 - 1

Verse 3:

Traffic lights keepin' time;
Leading the wild and restless
Through the night.

Verse 4:

Spinning 'round, in a spell;
It's hard to leave this carousel.
'Round and 'round and 'round and 'round.

ESCAPE

Words and Music by
S. PERRY, N. SCHON and
J. CAIN

26

don't un-der-stand;___ turns a boy in-to a fight-in' man.___

They___ won't take me;___ they___ won't break me.___

Oh,_____ now he's leav - in'; get - tin' out from this

mas - quer - ade._____ Oh,_____ got-ta go.

N.C.

1. To next strain
A/C#
2. fine

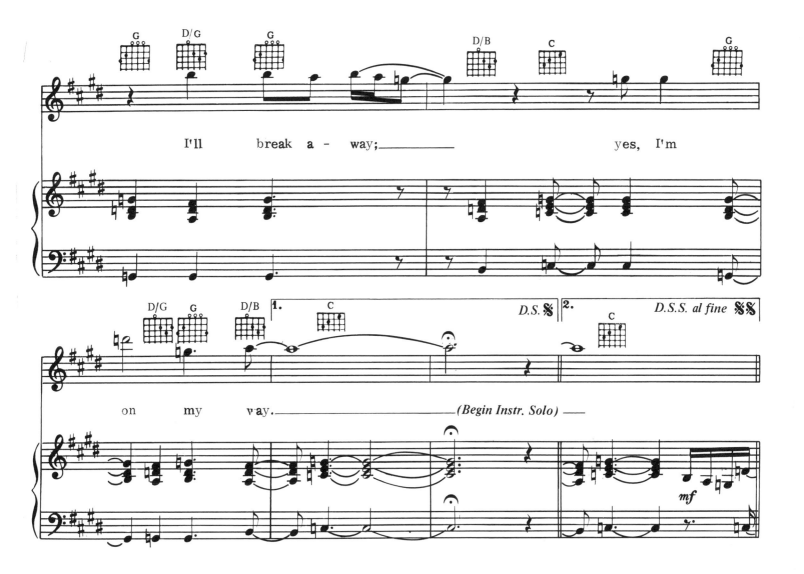

Verse 2:
No one could tell him what to do;
Had to learn everything the hard way.
He's on the street, breakin' all the rules.
I'm tellin' you that he's nobody fool.

Bridge 3:
Just when you think you had it all figured out;
Runnin' scared can change your mind.
I never knew I had so much to give;
How hard times can fool ya'.

Bridge 4:
Oh, I'm okay, I'm all right;
Feeling good out on your own.
I'll break away, I'll break away tonight;
I've got dreams I'm living for.

LAY IT DOWN

Words and Music by
S. PERRY, N. SCHON and
J. CAIN

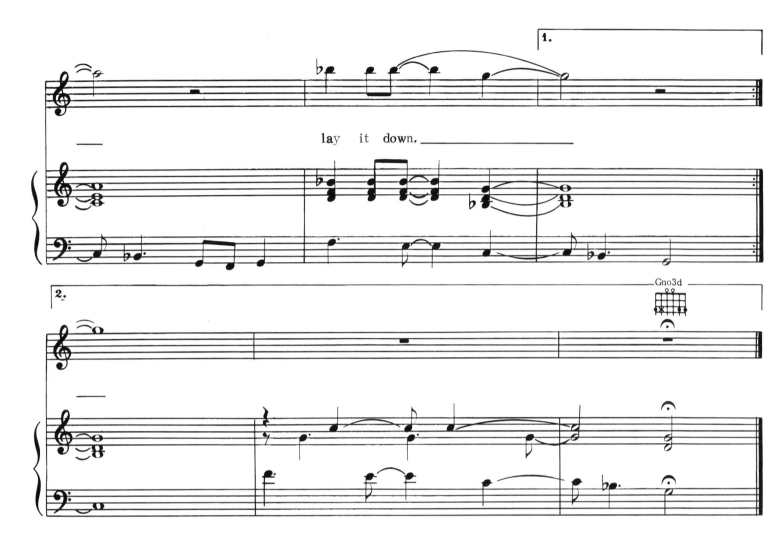

lay it down._____

Verse 2:
Whiskey, wine and women;
They get me through the night.
I ain't lookin' for trouble;
I ain't lookin' to fight.
A little vertical persuasion,
Would do me right.
What I'm really needin';
Ah, double shot tonight.

2nd Bridge:
By the midnight hour,
We were on our way.
She was takin' it higher;
Higher, higher, higher, then I heard her say:
(Chorus:)

3rd Bridge:
By the midnight hour,
We were on our way.
She was takin' it higher;
Higher, higher, higher, then I ... *(To Coda:)*

DEAD OR ALIVE

Words and Music by
S. PERRY, N. SCHON and
J. CAIN

Hard and Fast Rock

A dou - ble se - cret a - gent;   and he was paid to kill;

2.(see additional lyrics)

Dead Or Alive - 7 - 1

Want - ed._

Want - ed._

Verse 2:
He drove a Maserati;
Lived up in the hills.
A cat with nine lives that's gone
Too far to feel the chill.
He never thought it'd happen;
It was his last mistake;
'Cause he was gunned down by a
Heartless woman's .38.

MOTHER, FATHER

Words and Music by
N. SCHON, S. PERRY,
J. CAIN and M. SCHON

Moderately Slow

1. She sits a - lone, an emp - ty___ stare; a
2.3.(see additional lyrics)

Mother, Father - 5 - 1

46

Mother, Father - 5 - 3

Verse 2:
With dreams he tried; lost his pride;
He drinks his life away.
One photograph, in broken glass;
It should not end this way.

Verse 3:
Through bitter tears and wounded years,
Those ties of blood were strong.
So much to say, those yesterday's;
So now don't you turn away.

OPEN ARMS

Words and Music by
S. PERRY and J. CAIN

1. Ly - ing_____ be - side_____ you, here in_____ the dark; feel - ing your
2. Soft - ly_____ you whis - per, you're so_____ sin - cere. How could our

3. 4.(see additional lyrics)

heart beat with mine.
love be so blind?_____

1. We
2.(see additional lyrics)

Open Arms - 3 - 1

Bridge:
Em
Bm
A/C♯
D
sailed on to- geth - er; we drift- ed a - part; and here you
A
G
A/G
G
are by my side. So, now I
Chorus:
D
F♯m
come to you with o - pen arms;
here I am with o - pen arms;
f
G
1.3. C
noth - ing to hide, be - lieve what I say. So,
hop - ing you see what your

love means___ to me;___ o-pen arms.   love means___ to

me;___ o-pen arms.

Verse 3:
Living without you; living alone,
This empty house seems so cold.

Verse 4:
Wanting to hold you, wanting you near;
How much I wanted you home.

Bridge:
But now that you've come back;
Turned night into day;
I need you to stay.
(Chorus)